OPEN HIGHWAYS

a diagnostic and developmental reading program

SPEEDING AWAY

Helen M. Robinson

Marion Monroe

A. Sterl Artley

Charlotte S. Huck

William A. Jenkins

Ira E. Aaron

Linguistics Advisor, Andrew Schiller

SCOTT, FORESMAN AND COMPANY

CONTENTS

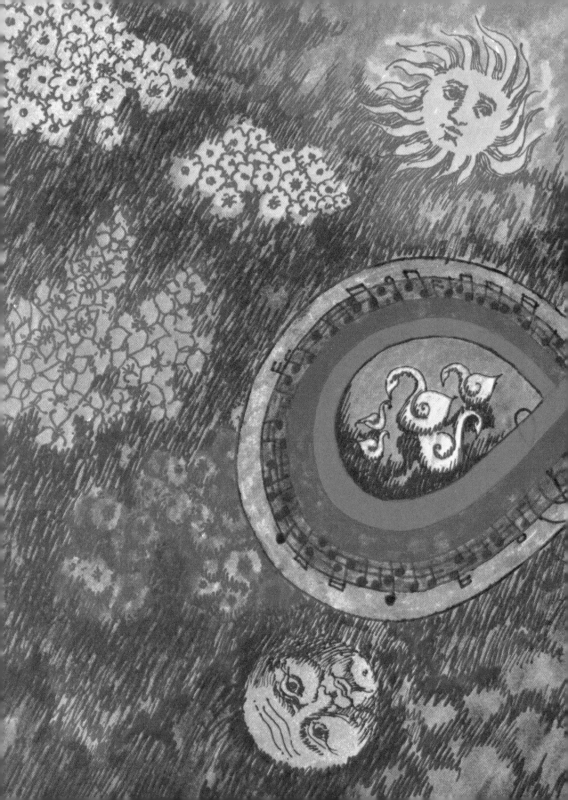

Clip-Clop

by Kathleen Vogt

There was
A horse trotting
That had a clip-clop beat
That lingers like a song upon
My mind.

"Cinquain" by Kathleen Vogt. Reprinted by permission of William Hurley.

SHADOW

by Howard E. Roberts

SHADOW OF SUNSET HILL FARM

There was a new colt at Sunset Hill Farm.
Mr. Rogers was excited. "Hurry!" he called
to his wife. "Come see the fine new colt."

Mrs. Rogers came running into the barn.
She looked into the horse stall.

"He looks strong and wide awake," she
said. "But his coat is a strange color!"

Mrs. Rogers thought for a minute. "Shadow!"
she said. "Let's call him Shadow of Sunset
Hill Farm."

Shadow was the son of Storm. Storm
was the World's Champion Tennessee Walking
Horse. Storm's rich dark coat was prettier
than Shadow's. But Mr. Rogers hoped that
Shadow's coat would darken. Shadow might
become a rare golden palomino. Perhaps
he would be famous!

As Shadow grew older, Mr. Rogers watched him closely. Shadow's coat changed to a dull yellow color. But the light coat did not worry Mr. Rogers yet.

Mr. Rogers was worried because Shadow never did the running walk. The running walk is the gait that made Tennessee Walking Horses famous. If Shadow could not do it, he could not be in a horse show. And Shadow did nothing but trot.

At last Mr. Rogers felt that Shadow would always be a trotter. So the yellow colt was turned out to pasture. He was almost forgotten.

About the time Shadow was a year old, a visitor came to Sunset Hill Farm. His name was Mr. Bates. He was a trainer of Tennessee Walking Horses. He was looking for a colt that he could train to be a world champion.

Mr. Rogers pointed out the colts that were for sale. Mr. Bates wanted two of them very much. But he thought their price was too high.

Mr. Rogers saw a chance to get rid of Shadow. "I'll give you the yellow colt if you buy the other two," he said.

Mr. Bates took a long look at Shadow. "It's a deal," he said.

Mr. Bates put the three colts into his horse van. When he got to his farm, his family was waiting for him.

"Hi, Dad," Lon called. "I'll open the van for you."

"Oh, Dad," cried Kitty. "I can't wait!"

Lon led the brown colt called Sunny Boy out of the van.

"He's beautiful!" Kitty cried.

Mr. Bates led the black colt out of the van. "This is Lucky," he said.

"They look like champions!" said Mrs. Bates.

Then Mr. Bates led Shadow out. Shadow began to trot around the corral. Everybody laughed.

"Where did you find the little yellow trotter, Dad?" Lon asked.

Mr. Bates smiled. "Go on and laugh," he said. "But this colt may be a world champion some day."

SHADOW'S NEW LIFE

Mr. Bates began to train the colts. Lucky and Sunny Boy did well. But Shadow still did not do the running walk.

After a long time, Mr. Bates gave up. He was sure that Shadow was not the colt to beat Champion Storm.

Shadow became Lon and Kitty's pet. They rode him around the corral. He followed them about like a puppy while they did their work.

The children fed and watered Shadow.
They groomed him. They took stones out of
his hoofs. They put clean straw in his stall.

As the months passed, Shadow's coat became
deep gold. His mane and tail were silver now.
He was a true palomino at last.

Mr. Bates looked at the beautiful pet who
would never step into a show ring. He shook
his head sadly.

One day Lon took Shadow out for a long ride. They walked up a narrow path. They crossed a fast stream. Shadow was sure-footed and strong.

When they came to open fields, Lon put Shadow into a trot. Then a wonderful thing happened. Shadow changed his gait. He lifted his front legs high at the knee. He reached far out with each step. This was the running walk. Shadow was a Tennessee Walking Horse after all!

Lon proudly showed his father Shadow's new gait. From that day on, Shadow was trained for the show ring.

Shadow seemed to know he was becoming important. He worked long and hard to please Mr. Bates. Soon he was ready for his first show at the state fair.

When Shadow entered the show ring, the crowd cheered. Shadow didn't mind the noise. He seemed to float around the ring. He did not break into a trot. He was steady as the judges looked him over. He easily won first prize.

Now Mr. Bates knew they were ready to take on Champion Storm. He entered Shadow in the famous Tennessee Walking Horse Celebration.

Mr. Bates worked with Shadow in the training ring every day. The whole family helped groom Shadow. Then they set off on the long drive to Tennessee.

The crowd at the Tennessee Walking Horse Celebration was excited. They went wild when Storm came into the show ring.

Another roar went up when Mr. Bates rode Shadow into the ring.

The other horses in the show were almost forgotten. Storm and Shadow fought for first place.

The crowd grew quiet as Storm and Shadow circled the ring again and again. Both were beautiful and strong. Both were well trained. Could one be better than the other?

It seemed hours before the judges picked
the winner. At last the ringmaster walked to
the center of the ring. He carried a silver
cup. He held up a blue ribbon.

The sound of a judge's voice filled the
air. Shadow was the new World's Champion
Tennessee Walking Horse!

A shout went up from the crowd.

Shadow seemed to move on wings as he
carried his master forward. Mr. Bates bent
to take the ribbon and the winner's cup.

Shadow proudly kept up the running walk
as he left the ring.

Soon Mr. and Mrs. Rogers came to Shadow's stall. "Congratulations," Mrs. Rogers said to the Bates family. "Shadow is a great new champion."

"And to think that I gave Shadow away!" said Mr. Rogers. "I just didn't see a winner in that little yellow trotter."

Shadow snorted. He stamped his feet and tossed his proud head. Kitty and Lon giggled. Then everybody laughed.

Kitty reached up to hug Shadow's neck. "We're so glad you gave him to us," she said to Mr. Rogers. "We love him."

Pecos Bill

by Tony Simon

Cowboys like to sit around the campfire and tell tall tales. Most often they tell about Pecos Bill. They say he was the greatest cowboy of them all.

Pecos Bill was born when the West was still wild. You might say he was a strange baby. He ate buffalo meat and cactus for breakfast.

20

A panther came into the cabin when Bill
was a baby. Bill's folks were working in
the fields. They heard the panther's roar.
They were sad.

"We are too far away to save the panther's
life," they said to each other.

Bill was sitting on a new panther rug
when his folks got home. He was eating a
panther bone.

Bill's mother was cross. She did not like
him to eat between meals.

Pecos Bill became sheriff of the whole
West when he grew up.
In his spare time he invented things.

chaps

barbed wire

roping

six-guns

branding irons

Before Bill invented roping, a cowboy would put a loop of a rope on the ground. Then he put food inside the loop as bait. He would wait for a steer to come by and step inside the loop. Sometimes a cowboy had to wait for weeks!

"That's no way to rope a steer!" Pecos Bill said. So he invented the lariat. His own lariat was so long it went around the world. Some cowboys say it was four feet shorter than that. But they all said Bill could rope anything from here to China.

Another of Bill's famous inventions was the bullwhip. One day a ten-foot rattlesnake struck at him.

"You asked for it," Bill said. "We'll fight it out fair and square. You can have the first three bites."

The snake bit Bill three times. But Bill didn't blink an eye. He just squeezed the snake's head between two big muscles on his left arm.

"Uncle," the snake yelled.

"Say, you would make a good whip," Bill told the snake.

Just then the king of the wowsers jumped
on Bill from a cliff. A wowser was part
bear and part mountain lion. But it was
ten times bigger than both.

Bill stood 1300 coyote paws high himself.
Bill and the wowser fought for hours. Bill
pulled out all the wowser's fur. There was
so much fur flying, people thought there was
an eclipse of the sun.

Then Bill jumped on top of the wowser.
The wowser arched its back twenty-seven feet
high. But Bill cracked his rattlesnake whip.
He rode the wowser up and down the mountains.

"Yippee!" Bill yelled. And that was the
first time a cowboy had ever said that.

Of course Bill's favorite rides were on his own mustang. Bill's mustang was so wild it could flip a rider to the moon. Its favorite food was dynamite.

Bill roamed far and wide on his mustang. Wherever they went, they left tales of how Pecos Bill helped build up the West.

Tall Tales About Strange Critters
by Tony Simon

HODAG

This lazy critter leans against a tree to
sleep. That is why so many trees grow crooked.
The Hodag is so heavy it pushes them over.

Reprinted by permission of Scholastic Magazines, Inc., from *Ribsnorters and Ribticklers*
by Tony Simon, Copyright © 1958 by Tab Books, Inc.

GOOFUS BIRD

This critter always flies backwards.
It likes to see where it has been — not where
it is going. It doesn't care where it's going.
It wants to get to where it went.

The Desert

by Justina Ignacio

The desert is a lonely place,
   it is lonely,
   but I do not mind.
It is my home.
It is peaceful.
   It is quiet.
It is beautiful.
The desert is a lonely place,
   but I do not mind
   because it is my home.

The Day in the Desert
by Lupe Pedro

I love the morning,
    its cool dawning,
    its birds singing
    and the sun peeping out
    with its shining ray.
I love the noon
    with its stillness
    and its cool shades,
    yet the hot winds blowing
    in the desert sand.
I love the evening,
    its colored sunsets,
    its singing breezes
    and the cactus shadows.
I love the desert,
    its night birds singing
    in the bright moonlight
    with the shining stars
    of the night.

Chuka's Hawk

by Elizabeth B. Whitmore

Chuka played on the roof of his house on the mesa. He saw Big Brother come up the trail from the desert.

Big Brother climbed the ladder to the roof.

Adapted by special permission from *Jack and Jill* Magazine, © 1964 The Curtis Publishing Company.

Chuka was unhappy. He went to Grandfather.

I want a pet eagle. Will you help me catch one, Grandfather?

Your brother's eagle will never be a good pet. But you could tame a hawk.

The next morning Chuka and Grandfather walked to the bird graveyard. They put a prayer stick on a rock.

I hear birds!

Those are hawks. We are in a good place. We will look for a hawk's nest.

At last Chuka saw a young hawk on a
tree branch. He took off his shirt. He
caught a grasshopper. He threw it on the
ground in front of the hawk. The hawk
flew down to eat it.

Grandfather came back. He had
found nothing.

They tied the hawk to the housetop.
Chuka named him Wiki. The hawk grew
to like Chuka. After a few weeks, Chuka
untied Wiki.

> Let's go for a walk, Wiki.

> Your hawk will fly away. It will never come back.

Wiki saw other hawks in the sky. He
flew up to them. Chuka was afraid Wiki
would never return.

> Oh, my hawk! You did come back. You choose to stay with me.

35

It was time for Big Brother to learn
to weave blankets. Grandfather would
teach him. Father would herd the sheep.

Come with me, Chuka.
It's time for you to help
herd the sheep. And bring
your dog, Bakito.

Father showed Chuka how to find grass and
water for the sheep. Bakito learned to keep
the flock together.

You have done well these
many weeks. You are ready to
herd the sheep without me. I
am needed in the fields.

It was lonely in the desert. So Chuka
took Wiki with him every day. But one day
both Wiki and Bakito left the herd.

A hungry coyote crept into the flock.
It snarled and dashed at the sheep. The
sheep ran wild.

Wiki heard. He shot down from the sky like an arrow. He dug his claws into the coyote's back. He bit the coyote.

The coyote howled and ran away.

Chuka told the family about his adventure.
Chuka's father was pleased.

Big Brother gave Chuka his best arrow.

Sand Painting

by Peggy Parish

Some Indians made sand paintings for the ceremonies of their tribes.

They drew designs on the ground with colored sand. They thought these designs would keep evil spirits away.

Sand paintings may be made on paper with cornmeal and glue.

You will need:

		white cornmeal
pencil	paper	small bowls
spoons	glue	food coloring

Material adapted from *Let's Be Indians* by Peggy Parish. Copyright © 1962 by Margaret Parish. Harper & Row.

Put some cornmeal into each bowl.
Pour a little food coloring over the
cornmeal. Use a different color for
each dish. Mix the food coloring and
cornmeal together.

Draw a design on the paper with the
pencil. Spread glue on one part of the
design. Sprinkle one color of cornmeal
over the glue.

Let the glue dry. Then slide the extra
cornmeal off the paper.

Sprinkle cornmeal on the rest of the
design in the same way.

The Story of William Penn

by Aliki

Specially adapted from the book *The Story of William Penn* by Aliki Brandenberg.
© 1964 by Aliki Brandenberg. Published by Prentice-Hall, Inc., Englewood Cliffs,
New Jersey.

Many years ago there lived a man all the
world came to know. His name was William
Penn.

William lived in England with his wife
and children.

William won many friends by being kind
and wise. Some of them were plain people.
Some were noblemen. One was the King of
England himself.

William had a lot of money. But he did
not choose to lead the life of a rich man.
He wore no frills. He was a simple man.
He liked people because they were good, not
because they were rich.

William was a Quaker. The Quakers are
gentle, peaceful people. They do not believe
in fighting. They think that all men should
live side by side as brothers.

But in those days, English people were not
free to say what they thought. They had to
speak carefully, or they were sent to jail.

William Penn was not afraid. He told the
people to believe what they thought was right.
He told everyone about freedom.

William was sent to jail for a while because he spoke so freely. Yet he never lost his hope. He thought all men could live together as brothers.

Now the King owed William a huge sum of money. It was time for the King to pay this money back. He gave William a big piece of land in America instead of money.

William had heard of the New World. He knew people had gone there to find a better life. He had dreamed of going there himself.

William set to work. He found people to go with him. He told them that in America they would be free. They could think and speak as they pleased.

William's new land was named Pennsylvania — the woods of Penn.

William planned where a city would be built. He planned where its homes would be. And he named it Philadelphia — the city of brotherly love. Finally all the plans were made.

William said good-by to his family. They
would join him later.

The sails were spread. The brave people
left their country.

The trip was long. The ship moved slowly. It rocked and tossed on the big waves. Many people became sick. Everyone wanted the trip to end.

Two long months passed.

Then one day, they saw a new land. They saw wigwams among the trees. Far away, Indians watched them.

People who had come earlier stood on the shore. They welcomed the new settlers with great joy.

But the Indians were worried. Many of their people had been chased from the land. Many had been hurt by other settlers.

William wanted to make friends with the Indians. He did not want them to be afraid of him and of his people. So he asked the Indians to a meeting.

The Indians came. They wore their finest feathers. They sat with the settlers in the shade of an old elm tree.

The settlers and the Indians gave each
other gifts. William wrote a peace treaty.

The treaty said: Our two peoples
will live together in respect and freedom.

The Indians trusted William because he was
fair to them. He did not chase them from
their land. He bought it from them.

He visited their homes. He respected their
way of doing things.

He learned to speak their language. He
said it was the most beautiful language of all.
William's city grew. New settlers came.
William Penn proved to the world that men
can live as brothers, if they want to.

Indian Steelworkers

The men in these pictures are Mohawk Indians. They are steelworkers. Many of the best steelworkers in the world are from the Mohawk tribe.

These men are making the skeleton of a skyscraper. They walk along the beams as if they were walking on the sidewalk. They are brave and tough and nimble.

This steelworker rides an elevator
halfway to his work. Then he must climb
swaying ladders to the top floors.

"Heights make him dizzy."

61

The People Downstairs

by Rhoda W. Bacmeister

The Sherrills lived on the fifth floor of an apartment building. There were lots of stairs to climb. But the Sherrill children liked their apartment. It was easy to go to the roof from the fifth floor.

Cathy and George and Joey Sherrill played on the roof with the Flannigan children from the fourth floor. But one day the Flannigans moved away, and some new people moved in.

63

Adapted by permission of Coward-McCann, Inc. and McIntosh and Otis, Inc. from *The People Downstairs and Other City Stories* by Rhoda W. Bacmeister. Copyright © 1964 by Rhoda Bacmeister.

SSSH-H-H-H-H-H-H!

Cathy knocked on the door of the
fourth-floor apartment. She hoped some new
children lived there. The door opened a crack.

"Shhh," a voice said. The door closed.

Cathy told her mother what had happened.

"Maybe someone is sick," Mother said. "I'll
go down to see if I can help. You take care
of the boys."

The boys and Cathy played a bean-bag
game. They jumped and laughed.

"Shhh!" said Mrs. Sherrill the minute she came back in the door. "We'll have to be quiet. Please play your game on the roof. After lunch we'll go for a walk. Then we'll read stories. But I do wonder when I'll get my work done."

When Mr. Sherrill came home, he tossed Joey up in the air. Joey shouted with joy.

"Shhh," said Mother.

"What's the matter?" asked Dad.

"Oh, dear," said Mother. "It's the people downstairs."

Mother said, "The man works at night. He has to sleep most of the day. Their baby has to have naps. And the woman is very jumpy."

"Hmmm, I see," said Dad. "They need a lot of quiet, don't they?"

"They sure do!" said Cathy.

"We can't do anything now!" said George.

"Well," said Dad in a loud voice. "The people downstairs must be awake by now. We can have some fun." He began to tickle George. Everyone had fun till 7:00 o'clock.

"The baby downstairs goes to bed now," said Mother.

Cathy and George and Joey had to be quiet part of every day. It got too cold to play on the roof or go to the park. The children tried to play quiet games inside the apartment. But sometimes they all got very cross. If they did make noise, the people downstairs banged on the pipes.

"They make more noise than we do," said
George with a frown.

"Come on," said Cathy. "I'll read you a
long story."

When Dad came home each night, he tried to
cheer everybody up. He made up a poem:

Oh, the people downstairs

Sleep longer than bears.

We must walk on our toeses

And not blow our noses,

Or we'll ruin the dozes

Of the people downstairs.

Then one wonderful day a truck came. The
people downstairs moved away.

Another family moved in. What a noise
they made! Four children ran up and down
the stairs. A wiggly puppy barked and
barked and got in the way.

Cathy and the boys watched from the
fifth floor landing. They called Dad and
Mother. The whole family danced in a circle.
They made up a song:

They've got girls and boys.

And they really love noise.

HURRAH FOR THE PEOPLE DOWNSTAIRS!

I Know an Old Lady
(Who Swallowed a Fly)

I know an old lady who swallowed a fly.
I don't know why she swallowed a fly.
I guess she'll die.

I know an old lady who swallowed a spider.
That wriggled and wriggled and tickled inside her.
She swallowed a spider to catch the fly.
But I don't know why she swallowed the fly.
I guess she'll die.

I know an old lady who swallowed a bird.
Now how absurd, to swallow a bird!
She swallowed the bird to catch the spider.
That wriggled and wriggled and tickled inside her.
She swallowed the spider to catch the fly.
But I don't know why she swallowed the fly.
I guess she'll die.

I know an old lady who swallowed a cat.
Now fancy that, to swallow a cat!
She swallowed the cat to catch the bird.
Now how absurd, to swallow a bird!
She swallowed the bird to catch the spider.
That wriggled and wriggled and tickled inside her.
She swallowed the spider to catch the fly.
But I don't know why she swallowed the fly.
I guess she'll die.

I know an old lady who swallowed a dog.

My what a hog, to swallow a dog!

She swallowed the dog to catch the cat.

Now fancy that, to swallow a cat!

She swallowed the cat to catch the bird.

Now how absurd, to swallow a bird!

She swallowed the bird to catch the spider.

That wriggled and wriggled and tickled inside her.

She swallowed the spider to catch the fly.

But I don't know why she swallowed the fly.

I guess she'll die.

I know an old lady who swallowed a goat.

Just opened her throat and in walked a goat!

She swallowed the goat to catch the dog.

My what a hog, to swallow a dog!

She swallowed the dog to catch the cat.

Now fancy that, to swallow a cat!

She swallowed the cat to catch the bird.

Now how absurd, to swallow a bird!

She swallowed the bird to catch the spider.

That wriggled and wriggled and tickled inside her.

She swallowed the spider to catch the fly.

But I don't know why she swallowed the fly.

I guess she'll die.

I know an old lady who swallowed a horse.

She's dead, of course!

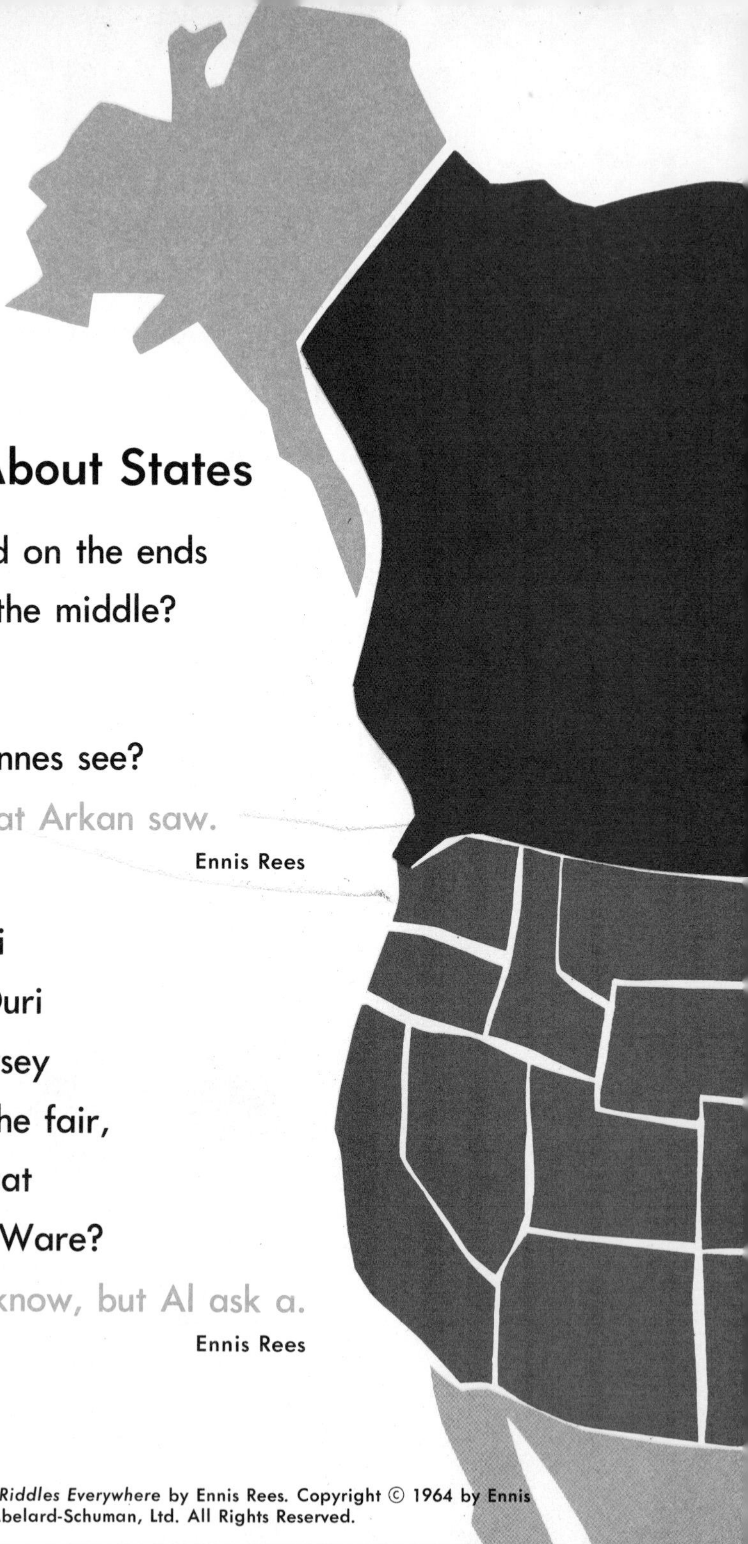

Riddles About States

What's round on the ends
And high in the middle?

O hi O

What did Tennes see?

Just what Arkan saw.

Ennis Rees

If Miss Issippi
Gave Miss Ouri
Her New Jersey
To wear at the fair,
What, oh what
Would Dela Ware?

I don't know, but Al ask a.

Ennis Rees

74

A Great Land

Alaska means "a great land" in the Aleut language.

Aleuts and Indians and Eskimos were the first people to live in Alaska.

Now Alaska is the biggest state in the United States of America. It is so big that people must often use airplanes to get from place to place.

Some people use dog sleds to go shorter distances.

Alaska has huge mountains and forests.
It has big cities and tiny villages too.
Many different kinds of people live together
in Alaska today. But they don't begin to
fill up the great land.

Eskimos live in villages throughout Alaska.
Alaskan Eskimos once lived in sod-covered
houses, but never in snow houses.

They build boats called kayaks out of wood
and stretched animal skins.

Eskimos must hunt for a living. Many kinds
of animals live in Alaska. Brown bear,
mountain sheep, and walrus are found there.

The polar bear is the king of the snow and
ice world.

The Wind from the Sea

by Ruth Belstorf

Onak and his father were harnessing the dogs to the sled.

Father looked at the sky. "The wind talks loud from the east," he said.

Adapted by special permission from *Jack and Jill* Magazine, © 1967 The Curtis Publishing Company.

"The ducks will fly now," Father said.
"We must go to the shooting station."

Onak could hardly wait to start. The
shooting station was ten miles away from the
village. Huge flocks of ducks flew over it
when they went south for the winter. Each
year Eskimo hunters shot some ducks for food.

Father and Onak went into their house.
Grandfather had oiled the gun. He handed it
to father.

"I cannot go on this hunt," Grandfather
said. "The leg I hurt yesterday is too stiff."

"Poor Grandfather," thought Onak. "He
will need care."

"I will stay behind," Onak said out loud

"So it will be," said Father. "You speak
as a man, my son."

Onak watched the sled until it was out
of sight. Then he hurried in to Grandfather.

"The wind comes in with you, Onak,"
said Grandfather. "Does it blow from the
sea now?"

"Yes, Grandfather," said Onak. "The wind
has changed."

"Then I fear no ducks will pass over the
shooting station," said Grandfather. "One
time, long ago, the wind turned suddenly.
We saw no ducks that year."

Onak sighed as he fixed the supper.
Grandfather talked much of long ago.

"When I am a man I will think of what is
new, not what is old," Onak thought. "It is
the new that is good."

Grandfather and Onak ate boiled fish.
Then they slept. Onak dreamed he was waiting
with his father at the shooting station. The
ducks came like a black cloud. They thundered
over the beach.

Onak woke with a start. "I was dreaming,"
he said to himself. But he listened. He
did hear the ducks!

"Grandfather," he called. "Listen!"

"I hear them, Onak," Grandfather said.
"The wind from the sea has brought the ducks
over us. The hunters will bring no food for
the winter."

"If only we had a gun here," Onak said.

"Eskimos had no guns long ago," Grandfather
said. "They hunted ducks with the bola."

"Grandfather!" shouted Onak. "Can we
make a bola?"

"We will try," said Grandfather. "Give
me some hard wood. I will carve balls for the
bola. You must cut thongs from a sealskin."

Grandfather carved three balls and drilled holes in them. He put the thongs through the holes. Then he braided the thongs into a handle.

It was light now. Onak ran out to practice with the bola. He whirled it around his head as Grandfather had told him to do. But he moved too fast. He jerked the bola. The bola wrapped itself around Onak's arm.

"This bola is no good to me," he cried. "I wish I had a gun!"

Onak saw a long black line in the sky.
Another flock of ducks was coming over.
This time he whirled the bola slowly at first,
then faster and faster. He let it go.

Up, up the bola went. It spun into the
flock. It fell, bringing down two ducks.

Onak threw again and again. He grew
tired and hungry. The wind was cold!
But Onak did not rest until the flocks
stopped coming.

He carried his ducks to the storehouse.
Then he ran to tell Grandfather what had
happened.

"There will be food for all of us," Onak
said.

"Then you threw the bola well," said
Grandfather.

"You know much, and I know little," Onak
told Grandfather. "But I have learned this
truth from you. Old ways are good ways, too."

Go Wind

by Lilian Moore

Go wind, blow
Push wind, swoosh.
Shake things
take things
make things
fly.

Ring things
swing things
fling things
high.

Go wind, blow
Push things — —wheee.
No, wind, no.
Not me —
not me!

A Candle in the Night

A NORTH AFRICAN LEGEND

Yasu and his friends were sitting around
the fire in Yasu's house. The wind whistled
outside. Icy snow hit the windows. It was
a good night for telling stories.

"The Candle Gives Out Heat" from *Stories From the Near East* by Leslie W. Leavitt.
Published by Longmans, Green & Co., Limited.

Soon each man was telling about the brave deeds he had done. Yasu listened to his friends at first. But soon he grew tired of all this empty talk.

"I'm as brave as any of you," Yasu said.

His friends laughed. Yasu did not seem brave.

"What can you do?" one friend asked. "How can you prove that you are brave?"

"I will stay out in the snow all night," Yasu said. "I will use no fire to warm me."

"You will freeze!" cried Yasu's friends.

Yasu's friends begged him not to do such a foolish thing. "We were only talking to pass the time," they said. "There is no need to prove that you are brave."

"No," said Yasu. "I know I can stay out all night. I will prove it. I will cook dinner for you tomorrow if I fail."

Yasu's friends went home to their warm houses. Yasu went out into the snow. The air felt like ice. Yasu shivered. He walked up and down the street. The whole town was still.

It grew colder and colder. The snow got so deep that Yasu could not walk. Yasu was sleepy. But he knew he would freeze if he fell asleep. He stamped his feet and rubbed his hands.

The lights in the houses of the town went out. Yasu could not even see the stars.

"How dark the night is!" Yasu thought.

Just then a candle gleamed in a window.

The candle was far away. Yasu could
barely see it. But it was warm and friendly.
The little flame was a sign that he was not
alone. Other people were up in the night.
    Yasu watched the candle every minute.
At last the night was over.

Yasu's friends came to see him the next day. "Did you stay out all night without a fire?" they asked.

"I stayed out all night, and I had no fire," Yasu said. "I thought I might have to give up. Then I saw a candle in a window. It helped me to stay awake."

"Then you did have heat!" cried Yasu's friends. "A candle gives off heat!"

Yasu snorted. "I could hardly see the candle," he said. "It was far away. It could not keep me warm."

Still, Yasu's friends said he owed them a dinner because a candle gives off heat. At last Yasu agreed to cook for them.

That evening Yasu's friends came to his house. "Is dinner ready?" they asked.

"Dinner is not ready yet," said Yasu. "But please sit down." His friends waited and waited. They got very hungry. "Can we help you get dinner ready?" they asked.

"No, thank you," said Yasu.

Later Yasu's friends asked, "Could we eat part of the dinner now? We could eat the rest when it is ready."

"I'm sorry," said Yasu. "All the dinner is in one pot."

At last Yasu led his friends to the kitchen. They all crowded into the doorway. Then they stared at one another. Finally they began to laugh. And Yasu laughed too.

A big pot hung from the ceiling. A small candle was on the floor under the pot.

"I am sorry the food cooks so slowly," Yasu said. "But wait a little. I know a candle gives off heat. You told me so."

Snowy Coconut Treats

You will need:

a spoon

a knife

measuring spoons

a bowl

a measuring cup

2 tablespoons of
soft margarine

1/2 cup of brown
sugar

2 tablespoons of
flaked coconut

6 graham crackers

"Snowy Coconut Treats" from *Humpty Dumpty's Magazine for Little Children* (December 1967). Reprinted by permission of The Better Reading Foundation, Inc.

First put the margarine
into the bowl. Stir in
the sugar. Mix until
smooth.

Next stir the coconut
into the margarine and
sugar.

Last spread the mixture
on the graham crackers.

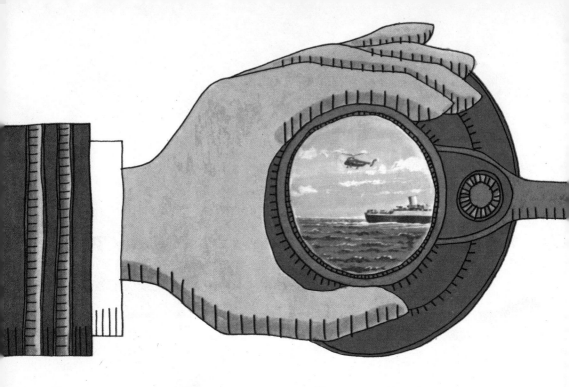

Pioneers in Space

by Helen Kay

Subject Number 65 had been shot into orbit in a space capsule. Who was Subject Number 65? No one would say. Would he ever come back alive? No one could know.

Ships were waiting. They sailed over the 300 miles of ocean where the capsule might land. Men watched the skies. It was very important to find the capsule and Subject Number 65.

102

From *How Smart Are Animals?* by Helen Kay, © 1962 by Basic Books, Inc., Publishers, New York.

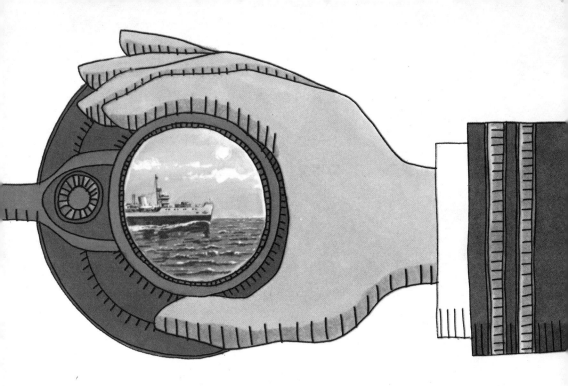

But something had gone wrong. The rocket
had shot the capsule forty miles too high.
A message was sent to the ships. The capsule
would not come down in the right place.

Planes took off from the ships. But they
saw no sign of the capsule. Only the blue
ocean gleamed below and the blue sky above.

At last a pilot saw something bright on
the sea. He flew down low, almost to the
water. Then he called his ship. "The capsule
is found," he said.

S/N '5'

Subject Number 65 was safe. He was strapped in his seat in the capsule. He was still pulling levers. He was doing the job he had been trained to do.

Only then could the secret be told. Subject Number 65 was a three-year-old chimpanzee. His name was Ham. He had freckles and a grin on his face.

Ham was taken out of the capsule. He shook hands with everybody. He ate an apple, an orange, and a banana.

Ham had proved that chimps are champs in space. He had done everything he had been trained to do. He had paved the way for the men who would follow him into space.

Local Boy Wins Spaceship

INDIANAPOLIS, IND. — Ten-year-old David Kahn filled out a coupon from a model kit. He sent it in to a contest. He won!

Yesterday he got his prize. The prize is a full-sized model of a real spaceship. But it doesn't fly.

"I've always wanted to go into space," David told reporters. "I'm going to find some way to make my ship fly."

The Ship from Zurn

The room was hot. David Kahn got out of bed and walked out onto the back porch.

"Maybe it's cooler out here," he thought. He sat down on the back steps. He rested his head on the railing.

Lights flashed over David's face. He covered his sleepy eyes with his hands.

"It's those mean kids upstairs," he thought. "Won't they ever get tired of bothering me?"

But suddenly David knew the lights were
coming from somewhere else.

He poked his head over the railing. And
five tiny heads poked back at his. Five
tiny men floated in the air. They glowed
a little in the dark.

"Oh! Wow! Don't go away," David said
softly. "I've been waiting to meet some
spacemen."

"We know. We know," soft voices said.
The voices sounded like faraway wind blowing.
"We will not go away yet, Giant Boy."

David giggled. Then he remembered all the
things he wanted to find out.

"Can I see your spaceship?" David asked.

"Not yet. Not yet," was the answer.

"I have a spaceship of my own, you know,"
David said in an important voice. He
couldn't help it.

"We know. We know," the little voices
sang softly.

"You know!" said David. "Do you read
earth newspapers?" The little men nodded yes.

"Why do you come to me?" asked David.
He was beginning to have a funny feeling.

One of the spacemen glowed brighter than
the others. He floated closer to David.
He seemed to be the leader.

"We have come to take your ship, Giant Boy,"
the leader said. "We need it for our mission."

"Take my ship!" David cried. "But I just
got it. I haven't even had time to work on
it. The whole town came to see it. And I've
been busy trying to keep the kids upstairs
from banging it up. Why, I was hoping you'd
help me make it fly."

"We can make your ship fly," the leader
said. "But we will fill it with ore and fly it
to our planet, Zurn. Our own ship is small.
And we have found much ore."

"What kind of ore?" asked David.

"Earth people do not know about it," the
leader said.

"If you take my ship to Zurn, I'm coming, too!" David said.

There was no answer. But the little men began to chant, "Take us to your ship."

Suddenly David moved off the porch. He didn't want to go. He leaned backwards, but his feet reached out. They walked him to his ship which was covered with a huge canvas. Then his feet stuck tight to the ground.

David's hands reached out. David tried
to stop them. But his hands pulled the heavy
canvas off the ship.

"Yes! Yes!" the little men said. They were
so pleased that they shot off sparks.

The leader turned to David. "We are
proud Zurns, Giant Boy," he said. "We will
not take your ship without payment. You will
see. We are fair."

"Fair!" shouted David. "You're not fair
at all!"

The door to David's ship swung open by
itself. The five little men floated in.

"You will see! We are fair," they sang.

David's ship lifted off with a WHOOSH!

"Come back!" David yelled. But his ship flew out of sight.

David could lift his feet again. He walked sadly toward the house. Suddenly there was a soft glow on the grass. The glow became a spaceship right before his eyes.

"What a great ship!" David cried. "It's the ship the Zurns came in. It must have been there all the time!"

He thought a minute. "This must be the payment the leader talked about," he said to himself. "The Zurns traded ships with me. But they didn't want me to follow them."

David opened the door of his new spaceship and stepped inside. He sat in the pilot's seat and looked at the controls — hundreds of controls!

"Oh, no!" David said. "This spaceship could go anywhere. But I don't know enough to fly it."

Then David's hands reached out by themselves.
They turned switches. They pushed buttons.
They pulled levers. The little ship began
to hum very softly.

"The Zurns are helping me!" David thought.
He grinned. "Thanks, Zurns!" he said out
loud. "You sure were fair!"

It was morning now. David looked out of
the porthole.

He could see the boys upstairs looking out
their window.

"Where's David's spaceship?" one boy
asked. "I was going to fool around with it
some more. It's fun to make David mad."

"I bet David had to give it to the museum,"
the other boy said. "He couldn't fly it if
he lived to be a hundred!" The boys left
the window.

David sat laughing in his new ship. "My ship's invisible!" he thought. "Those kids were looking right at it. And they didn't see it. I'm the only one who can see it. Oh boy!"

He pulled the stick. The little ship rose like a bird.

"And now —," David said out loud, "I think I'll fly around the world before breakfast."

WHO'S
IN
CHARGE
OF
LINCOLN?

BY DALE FIFE

Part I

Lincoln Farnum liked to pretend. So it was hard to believe all the things that happened to him.

Mom always listened to everything Lincoln told her. Pop listened to Lincoln, too. But he shook his head at some of Lincoln's stories. And Lincoln's sisters wouldn't believe anything Lincoln said.

Mom was on her way to the hospital. The new baby was coming two days early.

Pop was a railroad man. He was on a trip to Chicago. Sissy and Sassy were visiting Aunt Charlotte. Lincoln's sister Sara was about to go to Washington, D.C., with her class.

"Who's in charge of Lincoln?" Sara asked.

"Mrs. Readywell will be in charge of Lincoln," Mom said. "She said she'd come this morning just in case I needed her."

Mom waved as her taxi pulled away. "Good-by," she called. "I'll see you soon."

Inside the house, the telephone rang.
Lincoln ran to answer it. It was Mrs.
Readywell. She couldn't hear very well.
She thought Lincoln was Mom. "Hello,
Mrs. Farnum," she said. "A horse fell on me
when I was painting the bathroom. My glasses
are broken. I have to get new ones. I
can't come over until tomorrow afternoon."

Lincoln said, "Mom just left for the hospital." But Mrs. Readywell had hung up. "It doesn't matter," Lincoln thought. "I can't make her understand anyway."

Lincoln went to find Sara. "A horse fell on Mrs. Readywell," he said.

"No you don't, Lincoln," Sara said. "None of your tall tales now. I have to do some shopping. And the train for Washington, D.C., leaves at noon. Be good when Mrs. Readywell comes," she said in a bossy voice. She ran out the door with her suitcase.

Lincoln wandered into his bedroom. He looked at his little statue of President Lincoln. He felt President Lincoln was his friend.

"I wish I could go to Washington, too," he told the statue. "After all, my name is Lincoln. It's more important for me to go to Washington than someone named Sara."

Lincoln put on his coat and went out. He stood on the corner and wondered what to do.

Just then a man pushed a big paper bag
into Lincoln's arms. He jammed three five-
dollar bills into Lincoln's hand.

"Take my lunch to the train station,"
the man told Lincoln. "Meet me by the
ticket window." Then the man hurried on.

Lincoln looked at the three bills.

"Zowie!" he said. He raced to the train
station. Behind him there was a clatter of
bells. A police car raced by. Its siren
screamed.

Part II

Lincoln waited and waited at the station.
Finally he set the bag on the floor beside
him. It tipped over, and a bundle of bills
fell out. Lincoln looked inside. The bag
was full of money!

"Zowie!" said Lincoln. "What'll I do?"
He sat on the floor and tried to believe what
had happened to him. "I'll find a policeman,"
Lincoln thought. He grabbed the bag and ran
out of the station.

Officer Roberts was standing in a traffic
jam at the corner. He was the policeman
who helped children cross the street to school.
Lincoln held up the bag. "It's full of money!"
he shouted.

"I can't listen to your yarns today,
Lincoln," said Officer Roberts. "Take off."

"Well!" thought Lincoln. "But what shall
I do now? I wish I could ask Sara. She's
bossy. But she knows what to do."

Lincoln looked up at the clock on the station. "Zowie!" he said. "Sara's train hasn't left yet. I bet I can find her."

Lincoln ran back into the station. He looked up at the big board. The train to Washington was leaving in seven minutes on track four.

A big crowd stood at the train gate. The crowd closed around Lincoln and swept him through. There was the train to Washington. But where was Sara? Lincoln thought she must be on board.

Lincoln jumped on the last car and ran through the train. Sara wasn't there. Suddenly the train jerked. It began to move. It was too late to get off! Lincoln dropped into a seat. He felt like crying.

Lincoln's mind raced. "Maybe there's another train to Washington," he thought. "That's it! Sara will be coming on the next train." He felt much better.

He sat back and pretended. He pretended he was a secret agent in the Union Army. He was taking secret papers to President Lincoln in a paper bag. Maybe there was a spy on the train. Lincoln held the bag of money tighter.

"Tickets, please," a loud voice said.

It scared Lincoln. He looked up at the conductor. "Maybe he'll put me off the train," Lincoln thought. "And I'll never find Sara."

"I don't have a ticket," Lincoln said. "But I have money." He took two of his five-dollar bills out of his pocket.

"You're supposed to buy a ticket at the station," the conductor said. He gave Lincoln the change and turned away.

"Whew!" Lincoln said.

Finally the train pulled into Washington. Lincoln was the first one off.

Lincoln went up to a trainman. "When is the next train from New York?" he asked.

"No more trains from New York tonight," the trainman said. "But there was a special train for high-school classes. It came in twenty minutes ago."

"I've missed Sara!" Lincoln said to himself. "Now what will I do?"

Lincoln climbed back on the train to think. No one else was around. He settled into his seat again. He made a pillow of the bag of money and closed his eyes.

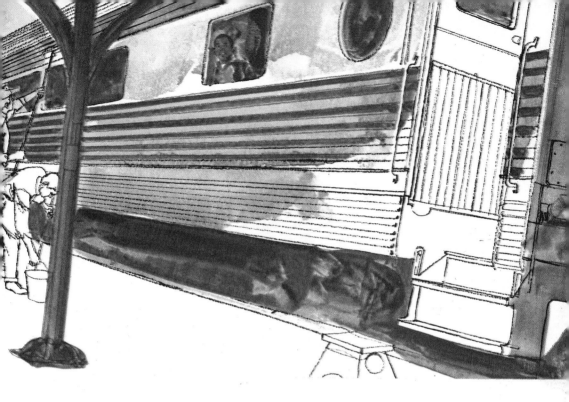

Part III

When Lincoln opened his eyes, it was morning.
Men were washing down the train. But no one
saw Lincoln jump off the last car. Lincoln
bought a hamburger for breakfast. Then he
felt ready for anything.

"I can find Sara," he thought. "I know
her class is going to the Lincoln Memorial.
Maybe she'll be there now."

He looked up and down the street. He wondered which way to go. A bus pulled up to the corner. "Do you go to the Lincoln Memorial?" Lincoln asked the bus driver.

"Sure thing," the bus driver said.

Lincoln climbed on the bus. He found a seat by the window so he could see the sights of Washington, D.C. He made up his mind to come back often and see everything. At the Lincoln Memorial, he got off the bus.

Lincoln walked up to the statue of President Lincoln. He looked into the face of the great figure.

Lincoln felt the President had been waiting for him. He looked kind and wise. Silently Lincoln told him everything that had happened.

The President seemed to listen carefully. He seemed to say, "You are a brave soldier, Lincoln Farnum. You have come a long way alone. I am proud of you."

Secret Agent Lincoln Farnum of the Union Army stood at attention. He saluted his President.

Just then a man walked by. He was wearing dark glasses. "He could be a spy!" thought Lincoln.

Secret Agent Lincoln Farnum took aim. He threw the bag of secret papers into the air.

The secret papers fell at the President's feet. Lincoln walked away from the statue before anyone knew what had happened.

Soon people saw the bag. They shouted to the guards and pointed. Lincoln saw the guards start to climb up to get the bag. He was sure they would know what to do with it.

Lincoln thought it was time to go home. There was no need to wait for Sara now. He had taken care of things himself.

Who was in charge of Lincoln? Why, Lincoln was. He took the train back home.

Mrs. Readywell was unlocking the front door when Lincoln got back. "Hello, there," she said. "I've come to take care of you. No one is home. I figure your Mom went to the hospital today."

"No," said Lincoln. "She went yesterday."

Mrs. Readywell didn't hear. She went into the kitchen.

"That's all right," Lincoln thought. He
picked up the paper to look at the headline:

NEW YORK BANK HAUL TURNS UP IN WASHINGTON

Who Tossed the Loot to Lincoln?

"I did," said Lincoln out loud. "But no one
will ever believe it."

Lincoln heard a key in the lock. Pop came
in. He looked very happy.

"I saw Mom," Pop said. "What do you
think we've got?"

Lincoln was afraid to hope.

Pop smiled and hugged him.

"It's a boy!" Pop said.

"At last!" Lincoln thought. "A brother!"

Some day he would tell his brother about his trip to Washington.

"Zowie!"

Glossary for Speeding Away

braid

capsule
(meaning 1)

capsule
(meaning 2)

A

arch bend into a curve: *The cat arched her back.* **arched, arch ing.**

B

bait anything used to attract fish or other animals so they may be caught: *Worms are good fishing bait.*

braid weave three or more pieces of material such as hair, leather, or ribbon together: *Every morning the little girl's mother braided her hair neatly.* See the picture. **braid ed, braid ing.**

C

can vas a strong cloth: *Our tent is made of canvas.* **can vas es.**

cap sule 1. a small case or covering, sometimes filled with medicine: *The doctor gave me capsules to take every three hours.* See the picture. 2. the part of a rocket that goes into orbit: *The capsule was in orbit for ten hours.* See the picture.

carve cut; make by cutting: *My father carved a doll from a piece of wood.* **carved, carv ing.**

134

chant to talk in a singsong way:
*The girls chanted a verse when
they jumped rope.* **chant ed, chant ing.**

chaps strong leather trousers, without
a seat, worn over other trousers by
cowboys: *When I ride through the
brush, I put on chaps to protect
my legs.*

coat any covering, such as a dog's
hair: *The dog's coat is black and shiny.*

con trol a button or switch that runs
a machine: *The pilot sat at the
controls ready for the take-off.*

cor ral a pen for horses, cattle, and
so on: *There were ten new horses
in the corral.* See the picture.

D

dawn the first part of day; the first
light in the east: *Dawn came at last.*

deed something done; an act; an
action: *To feed the hungry birds
is a good deed.*

dull not bright or clear: *The colt's coat
was a dull color until he was two
years old.* **dull er, dull est.**

E

ea gle a large, strong bird that can see
far: *An eagle builds his nest far off
the ground.*

corral

earth
(meaning 1)

eclipse

earth the planet on which we live, a great ball that moves around the sun: *The earth takes 365 days to go around the sun.* See the picture.

e clipse passing from sight because light is cut off. In an eclipse of the sun, the moon is between us and the sun, so that from any point within the moon's shadow on earth the sun is invisible: *You can hurt your eyes if you watch an eclipse of the sun.* See the picture.

F

fair[1] a show or sale, often of farm animals and things such as clothes and canned food: *Our cow won a prize at the state fair.*

fair[2] not favoring one more than any other; honest: *A fair judge decided to let the man go.* **fair er, fair est. fair and square** just; honest: *Their team won the game fair and square.*

flock a group of animals of one kind that stay together: *We watched a flock of geese fly past.*

G

gait the kind of steps used in going along; manner of walking: *He has a lame gait because of an injured foot.*

136

gleam send out a light; shine: *The flashlight gleamed in the dark.* gleamed, gleam ing.

groom feed and take care of (horses); rub down and brush: *Grooming a horse is a hard job.* groomed, groom ing.

H

har ness 1. leather fittings for an animal which connect it to a carriage, plow, etc., or are used in riding. Reins, collar, and bridle are parts of a horse's harness: *We must repair the harness before we can ride the horse.* har ness es. See the picture. 2. put a harness on: *Please harness the horse.* har nessed, har ness ing

haul the amount won, taken, etc., at one time; catch: *The fishermen made a good haul today.*

herd 1. many animals together: *We saw a herd of elephants in the movie.* 2. take care of (cattle or sheep): *He herded the sheep on a hill.* herd ed, herd ing.

huge very, very large: *A whale or an elephant is a huge animal.* hug er, hug est.

I

in vis i ble not able to be seen: *Germs are invisible without a microscope.*

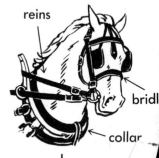

reins

bridl

collar

harness

J

jam 1. a crowded mass: *What a traffic jam!* 2. press or squeeze tight: *A crowd jammed into the bus.* jammed, jam ming.

join come together with: *Join us as soon as you can.* joined, join ing.

K

king 1. the man who rules a country and its people: *William Penn and the King of England were good friends.* 2. Something or someone best in its group: *The lion is the king of beasts.*

L

land ing a platform between flights of stairs: *The boy counted ten pairs of boots on the landings.*

lin ger stay on; go slowly, as if unwilling to leave: *She lingered after the others had left.* lin gered, lin ger ing.

loot something stolen: *The policemen found the loot from the jewelry store robbery.*

M

mane the long, heavy hair on the neck of a horse, a lion, and some other animals: *The Indians used to braid the horses' manes.* See the picture.

mas ter a person who rules or commands; the one in control: *The dog's master taught him to sit.*

138

me sa a small high plain with steep sides: *By standing on top of the mesa, the cowboy could count all the cows.* See the picture.

mis sion sending or being sent on some special work; errand: *The detective was sent on a secret mission.*

mus tang the small wild or half-wild horse of the North American plains: *The mustang he caught could not be tamed.*

mesa

nar row not wide: *The road was too narrow for us to pass another car.* **nar row er, nar row est.**

New World North America and South America: *Many tribes of Indians lived in the New World.* See the map.

nim ble quick moving; active and sure-footed; light and quick: *Goats are nimble at climbing rocks.* **nim bler, nim blest.**

New World

no ble high and great: *The duke was of noble birth.* **no bler, no blest.**

no ble man a man of noble rank, title, or birth: *The nobleman had many servants in his house.* **no ble men.**

or bit the path of a man-made satellite around the earth: *The capsule stayed in orbit for two days.* See the picture.

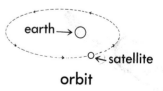

orbit

139

ore rock, sand, or dirt containing
    some metal: *The men are mining ore
    in that mountain.* ore.

P

pal o mi no a certain kind of
    cream-colored horse. Its mane and
    tail are usually lighter colored: *It is
    easy to see which horse is a palomino.*

pave prepare; make smooth or easy: *That
    experiment paved the way for others
    because we learned so much from it.*
    paved, pav ing.

pay ment something that is paid:
    *She baked a cake for us in payment for
    our help.*

pi o neer a person who goes first or does
    something first and so prepares a way
    for others: *He was a pioneer in the West.*

plain 1. common; ordinary; simple in
    manner: *He was a plain man of the
    people.* 2. a flat stretch of land:
    *Cattle wandered over the western
    plains.* plain er, plain est.

plan et one of the heavenly bodies that
    moves around the sun. Mercury, Venus,
    the earth, Mars, Jupiter, Saturn,
    Uranus, Neptune, and Pluto are
    planets: *Zurn is a make-believe planet.*

prai rie a large area of level or rolling land with grass but few or no trees: *Coyotes live on the prairies.*

R

rare not often found; few: *Peacocks are rare birds in the United States.* **rar er, rar est.**

re spect 1. thoughtfulness for others: *The boy has respect for his grandmother.* 2. show thoughtfulness for: *Respect the ideas of others.* **re spect ed, re spect ing.**

ring a closed-in space for races, games, or a show: *The horses pranced around the circus ring.* See the picture.

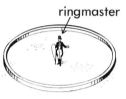

ringmaster

ring

ring mas ter one in charge of performances in a ring (as of a circus): *The ringmaster called for the next act.* See the picture for **ring.**

rock et a long tube that can shoot rapidly upward or forward: *Large rockets are used to explore space.*

S

sat el lite a man-made satellite is something shot into space on a rocket and goes around the earth in an orbit: *Satellites going around the earth help tell what the weather will be.* See the picture for **orbit.**

141

skyscraper

thong

set tle move to a new country or place: *The English settled in the New World.* **set tled, set tling.**

set tler a person who settles in a new country: *The early settlers in America had to fight the Indians.*

sim ple without ornament; not rich or showy; plain: *He eats simple food and wears simple clothing.* **sim pler; sim plest.**

six-gun a gun that can fire six shots without being reloaded.

skel e ton a frame: *The men are working on the steel skeleton of the building.*

sky scrap er a very tall building: *New York is famous for its skyscrapers.* See the picture.

snort 1. force the breath violently through the nose with a loud, harsh sound: *The horse snorted.* 2. say with a snort: *"Indeed!" snorted my aunt.* **snort ed, snort ing.**

start 1. begin to move: *Let's start for school now.* 2. move suddenly: *She started in surprise.* **start ed, start ing.**

T

tale a story: *The cowboys told us wild tales.*

thong a narrow strip of leather: *Thongs are good for lacing up heavy boots.* See the picture.

trea ty an understanding, especially one between nations, signed by each nation: *The settlers broke many of the treaties the government made with the Indians.* **trea ties.**

trot go as a horse does, lifting one front foot and one back foot at about the same time: *The horse trotted around the corral.* **trot ted, trot ting.**

trot ter a horse that trots.

U

un cle 1. the brother of one's father or mother or the husband of one's aunt: *My Uncle Jim is my mother's brother.*
2. used as a cry when giving up: *Tom twisted my arm till I yelled, "Uncle!"*

V

van a covered truck or wagon: *A van moved our furniture to the new city.*

W

whirl turn or swing round and round; spin: *The leaves whirled in the wind.* **whirled, whirl ing.**

wig wam a hut of poles covered with bark, mats, or skins, made by North American Indians: *We saw many wigwams in the Indian village.* See the picture.

wigwam

Y

yarn a tale; a story: *Cowboys tell the best yarns of the Old West.*

143

Acknowledgments

Book cover and title page designed by Bradford/Cout Graphic Design.

The illustrations in this book are by:

Bradford/Cout Graphic Design,
pages 4-5, 62-69
Lois Axeman, pages 6-19
Don Madden, pages 20-27
James Higa, pages 28-29
Phero Thomas, pages 30-31,
90-91
Ralph Creasman, pages 32-39
Bob Cooley, pages 40-41
Aliki, pages 42-57

Elizabeth Twig, pages 70-73
Lois Ehlert, pages 74-75
Phil Renaud, pages 82-89
Regina and Haig Shekerjian,
pages 92-99
John Magine, pages 100-101
Bob Binkley/John Magine,
pages, 102-103
Ed Broussard, pages 106-116
Bill Chambers, pages 117-133

The photographs in this book are gratefully acknowledged to the following:

Wide World, pages 58-59, 104
Chicago Tribune Photos, page 60
Doug Wilkinson, pages 76-77
Steve and Delores McCutcheon, pages 78, 79 (top left, top right, bottom right), 80
Fritz Goro - Life Magazine; Time, Inc., page 79 (bottom left)
National Film Board of Canada; Photo by Ted Grant, page 81
NASA, page 105

Grateful acknowledgment is hereby given for the right to use "The Desert" by Justina Ignacio, page 30, and "The Day in the Desert" by Lupe Pedro, page 31, from *The New Trail*. Reprinted by permission of the Bureau of Indian Affairs, U.S. Department of the Interior.

3 4 5 6 7 8 9 10 11 12 13 14 15 16 17 18 19 20 21 22 23 24 25 NR 75 74 73 72 71 70 69 68